*For all the kids out there writing
stories and drawing whenever you can:
keep going! I mean, look at this – it's a
whole book about a pig in a cape.
If I can do it, you can too!*

CHAPTER ONE

"LET'S DO THIS"

BATPIG WAS IN SERIOUS TROUBLE.

SIGH

In some serious doo-doo, aren't you, Mr. Batpig?

SSSSS

He was strapped to a giant rocket by the potty-mouth repto-man. And the fuse was lit!

ON THE ROOF OF A TALL BUILDING, THE ROCKET WAS AIMED RIGHT AT THE SUN.

This is so pooping awesome!

sss

AND HE'D SWALLOWED A POISON PILL, SO HE ONLY HAD MOMENTS TO DO SOMETHING!

THE SITUATION isn't ideal.

SSS

SUDDENLY, THE FUSE RAN OUT AND POOR BATPIG BLASTED OFF. REPTO-MAN YELLED SOMETHING POTTY-RELATED IN HIS EXCITEMENT.

OH, DEAR.

TOILET BRUSH!! YESSS!

AS THE ROCKET CLIMBED, BATPIG PLANNED...

FIRST, I need to barf up this poison pill!

HE HAD TO THINK OF SOMETHING GROSS ENOUGH TO MAKE HIM HURL.

Mustard and olive ice cream!

Mrs. HAWLEY'S TOENAIL COLLECTION!

WORM SPIT!

Worm spit did the trick.

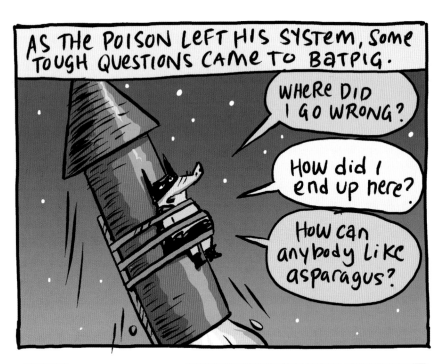

CHAPTER TWO

"STRANGE BEGINNINGS"

FLASHBACK ALERT!!

GARY YORKSHIRE WAS A PIG. A NORMAL, PINK, FUZZY, BORING OL' PIG...

Hey!

He lived with his parents (IMA AND URA) in a FOURTH-STORY WALK-UP IN BIG CITY, USA.

ARTSY PROFESSIONAL Family photo

He was a SIXTH GRADER AT BIG CITY MIDDLE SCHOOL, HOME OF the Fighting BURRITOS.

WORST MASCOT ever.

He liked what most pigs his age like: Tasty sandwiches...

Oh...oh OINK that's good.

PIG SODA

SLOP COOKIES

Video games...

SNORT **SNORT** SNORT SNORT.

Reading comics...

HAHA! THE CRIMSON SWINE DOES IT AGAIN!

Mud baths...

Playing cards with friends...

We should make some sandwiches.

IT WAS A PRETTY NORMAL LIFE, THERE IN THE FANCY TERRACE APARTMENTS.

UNTIL ONE AFTERNOON...

THEY MOSTLY PLAYED "GO FISH" 'CAUSE CARL WAS A FISH, SO HE LIKED THAT GAME.

IT WAS GETTING LATE AND CARL WAS GETTING KIND OF DRY. (HE'S A FISH, AFTER ALL.)

GARY LOOKED OVER AND SAW THAT BROOKLYN HAD NODDED OFF.

Ha ha! Good ol' BROOK.

Z.

HE DECIDED TO TRY THAT THING WHERE YOU PUT SHAVING CREAM IN HER HAND AND TICKLE HER NOSE.

Bat Snore.

Hee Hee. This is Gonna Be So GREAT!

She's Gonna Smear it ALL OVER HER...

BUT BROOKLYN WAS Startled AND Bit Gary RIGHT ON THE HONKER!

GAA!

YAAAA! MY HONKER!

CHOMP.

OH NO!! I THOUGHT YOU WERE a MOSQUITO!

DO I LOOK LIKE a MOSQUITO?

BEFORE BROOKLYN LEFT, SHE PUT SOME OINTMENT ON GARY'S SNOUT.

Sorry again, buddy.

It's okay. It doesn't hurt that bad.

MAN! I go to the john for one minute and miss all the good stuff!

THAT NIGHT, GARY'S SNOUT THROBBED, AND HE DREAMED HE WAS A BIRD.

This is a weird dream.

That's a weird beak.

THE NEXT MORNING, GARY FELT WEIRD, SO HE CALLED BROOK.

I feel weird. You don't have rabies, do you?

YOO HOO

No, and that's an offensive thing to ask a bat.

17

SAYING HE WAS WAS DOING HOMEWORK, GARY LAY DOWN FOR A QUICK NAP, BUT SLEPT UNTIL IT WAS DARK OUT.

THEN HE WAS WIDE AWAKE ALL NIGHT!

THE NEXT DAY, HE ATE, LIKE, TEN TASTY SANDWICHES.

GOODNESS, GARY.

URP.

WHEN HE PUT ON HIS UNDERPANTS, HE ACCIDENTALLY GAVE HIMSELF A WEDGIE.

IT'S LIKE I DON'T KNOW MY OWN STRENGTH!

AND OW!

LATER, JUMPING ON HIS BED, HE JUST KIND OF... STAYED IN THE AIR. FLOATING!

ULP!

THIS ISN'T NORMAL!

THEN, HE SAW RIGHT THROUGH THE WALL AND SAW MRS. HAWLEY'S GIANT COLLECTION OF CAT HAIRBALLS!

GROSS!

EH?

MEOW

AT LUNCH, He toLD BROOKLYN. (BUT NOT CARL. CARL WaS a gOOD FISH, BUT He COULDN'T Keep a SeCReT AT ALL.)

I think I have... LiKe... POWeRS!

WHAT? Hey! STOP WHiSPeRING!

BROOKLYN thoughT He'D LOST IT...

I THiNK YOU'Ve LOST It.

I haven't lost it.

LOST WhaT??

20

So that AFTERNOON (WHILE CARL WAS at his TROMBONE LESSON) GARY SHOWED BROOKLYN WHAT WAS UP.

22

BUT GARY SOON SAW THE UPSIDE.

I'm Like the CRIMSON SWINE!

It's Both EXCITING AND tERRIFYING!

GARY SPENt the night reading OVER ALL OF HiS OLD CRIMSON SwiNe comic books.

Hmm. My PoWeRS are different.

CRIMSON SWINE

more... Bat-like.

But Gary couldn't stop thinking about it.

AND THEN... HE HAD IT.

CHAPTER THREE

COOL POSE

"THEN AND NOW"

BUT, BACK to that
ROCKET HEADED to the SUN.
REMEMBER that?

BATPIG WAS HOTTER THAN A HABANERO POPPER, WHAT WITH THE SUN BEING SO CLOSE AND ALL.

HE WAS THINKING HE WAS A GONER WHEN HE SAW SOMETHING COMING.

ASTEROIDS! COMIN' RIGHT AT HIM!!

IT WAS BAD.

ONE GiAnt asteroid SlammeD
INTO THE tip OF BATPiG's Rocket,
KNOCKING it Off COURSE.

Sending Him hurtling toward a deadly crash into the earth.

But let's get back to our origin story, shall we?

So BROOKLYN agreed to train GARY... BUT from the GROUND.

35

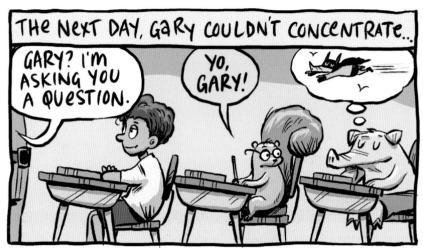

THE NEXT DAY, GARY COULDN'T CONCENTRATE...

GARY? I'M ASKING YOU A QUESTION.

YO, GARY!

HE HAD SO MANY THINGS TO TRY!

CAN I TOUCH A CLOUD?

CAN I SIT ON ONE?

WHAT DO CLOUDS TASTE LIKE?

I DON'T KNOW.

I DON'T KNOW.

I DON'T KNOW.

AND ALL THE BATPIG STUFF TO WORK OUT!

OH! I NEED A CATCHPHRASE, RIGHT?

WELL, OBVIOUSLY. TRY A FEW ON ME.

37

BROOKLYN SHOWED GARY SOME COSTUME IDEAS SHE'D BEEN WORKING ON.

THIS ONE'S NEAT.

HOW WOULD I GO TO THE BATHROOM IN THAT?

THIS? SNAZZY, RIGHT?

WAIT. IS THAT SPANDEX?

I ENJOY THIS ONE.

TOO SWIRLY.

At CARL'S PLACE...

CHAPTER FOUR

"WHAT ABOUT CARL?"

ONE DAY AFTER SCHOOL, CARL DECIDED TO FOLLOW BROOK & GARY. IN DISGUISE.

AT THE PARK, CARL HID IN SOME PLANTS AND WATCHED.

UNTIL GARY FLEW DOWN OUT OF THE FLIPPIN' SKY!!

42

44

45

SO GARY...ER...BATPIG DID.
HE SET OFF INTO THE NIGHT!

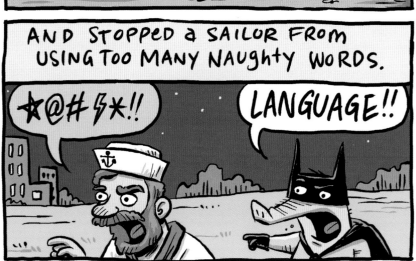

FLYING BACK TO BROOKLYN'S HOUSE, GARY NOTICED A LIGHT ON IN CARL'S BEDROOM.

AND WHAT HE SAW IN CARL'S WINDOW MADE HIM FEEL AWFUL.

HE FLEW BACK IN A RUSH.

OH, AND IN THE PRESENT, BATPIG IS STILL SPEEDING TOWARD CERTAIN DOOM, YADDA YADDA YADDA...

CHAPTER FIVE

"PARTY TIME"

THE NEXT NIGHT, CARL WORE HIS BEST SWEATER FOR THE PARTY.

THERE YOU GO. THAT'S A FISH WHO'S READY TO PARTY.

HE SHOWED UP AT GARY'S, READY FOR AN EXPLANATION AND SOME FUN!

THE OLD GANG. BACK TOGETHER AGAIN!

DING DONG

HE EVEN BROUGHT COOKIES AND A COUPLE OF HIS NEW MAGIC TRICKS.

MAGIC STUFF

IT WAS A GREAT PARTY, CONSIDERING IT WAS JUST THE THREE OF THEM.

HAA!

YOU SMASHED ME! I'VE BEEN MUSHED!

THEY PLAYED VIDEO GAMES.

SO TASTY!

BEYOND TASTY!

THEY ATE TASTY SANDWICHES.

MMPH!

BUT FINALLY, CARL ASKED HIS BIG QUESTION.

SO... WHAT HAVE YOU GUYS BEEN SO BUSY WITH?

SO, THEY DID. BADLY. THEY JUMPED AND ROLLED AROUND ON THE FLOOR, MAKING IT UP AS THEY WENT.

IT WAS SOME OF THEIR SUPERHERO NOTES.

AND SOMETHING SNAPPED IN CARL.

60

61

CHAPTER SIX

"A HERO IN ACTION"

PROWLING FOR TROUBLE, OUR CAPED HERO...

HELP!!

WHAT'S THAT? AN ACTUAL CRY FOR HELP?

WITHOUT HESITATION, BATPIG FLEW TO THE RESCUE!

WHAT IF THERE'S, LIKE, REAL BAD GUYS?

OKAY, THERE WAS SOME HESITATION.

66

BATPIG USED HIS MOVING-STUFF-WITH HIS-BRAIN POWER TO DISARM AND CONFUSE THE CRIMINAL.

WHAT THE...?.

I'VE LOST MY BAD GUY WEAPON!

AND GRAVITY!

WHOA.

FEAR NOT! I'LL TAKE THIS HOODLUM TO THE POLICE!

THANK YOU, BATPIG!

EXCEPT FOR THE VOICE THING. THAT WAS AWKWARD.

BatPig floated the baddie straight to the authorities.

And the police couldn't have been more excited.

CHAPTER SEVEN

SSSSS

PIG SODA

"THINGS GET WEIRD"

MEANWHILE, CARL WAS WORKING ON SUPERVILLAIN STUFF.

LET'S SEE. WHAT KIND OF EVIL DOES "THE FISHMONGER" GET UP TO?

OH, YEAH. HE'S CALLING HIMSELF "THE FISHMONGER" NOW.

I COULD JUMP OUT AND YELL BOO!

SHORT SHEET HIS BED!

REACH BEHIND HIS BACK AND TAP HIS SHOULDER SO HE'S ALL LIKE WHAAAAAA??

WITH GARY ON HIS WAY, CARL WHIPPED UP HIS HORRIBLE CREATION.

BUT LITTLE DID CARL KNOW, THE COMBO CAUSED A CHEMICAL REACTION!

AN AWFUL REACTION.

WHEN GARY ARRIVED, CARL MADE HIS SINISTER OFFER.

GARY, WOULD YOU LIKE A DELICIOUS PIG SODA?

NAH, I'M GOOD.

BUT YOU LOVE PIG SODA.

I JUST HAD ONE. PUT IT ON THAT SHELF FOR LATER!

THE SHELF ABOVE YOUR LIZARD!

AN ANGRY CARL PLACED THE SODA ON THE SHELF ABOVE HIS LIZARD.

BOOK OF POTTY JOKES STILL OPEN

MAGICIAN HAT & BOW TIE

AND HE SLAMMED HIS BEDROOM DOOR AS HE LEFT, TIPPING THE SODA.

SSSS

SSSSS

OH, DEAR.

CARL AND GARY WERE HAVING SUCH A GREAT TIME, CARL FORGOT ALL ABOUT THE SODA!

HEY! YOU CAN'T MUSH MY SMASHER AFTER A POWER-UP!

NO! I GOT RESMASH-INATED, REMEMBER?

THEN GARY HAD TO GO HOME, AND CARL FELT PRETTY GOOD ABOUT THINGS.

I FEEL SWELL!

THAT VILLAIN STUFF WAS DUMB ANYWAY.

BUT... WHAT HE FOUND IN HIS ROOM LEFT HIM STUNNED.

GASP!

77

BUT NOW I CAN HELP YOU DESTROY BATPIG! TWO SUPERVILLAINS WORKING TOGETHER!

"DESTROY" SEEMS LIKE A HARSH WORD.

WHAT?? AFTER HE LEFT YOU OUT? HIM AND THAT BAT?

LISTEN. I THINK I JUMPED THE GUN A LITTLE. GARY'S A GOOD GUY. AND BROOK'S AWESOME. I DON'T THINK THEY MEANT TO—

CHAPTER EIGHT

LIZARD
BREATH

"LIZARDS AND ROCKETS
AND STREET SIGNS.
OH MY!"

ABOUT THAT TIME, GARY WAS TELLING BROOKLYN ABOUT "BATPIG'S BIG NIGHT."

SO, YOU AND THE ROBBER FOUGHT?

ARE THERE MORE SAND- WICHES?

NO.

DANG.

BUT, YEAH! WE HAD A HUGE BATTLE.

MM-HMM. SO, WHY DON'T YOU HAVE ANY BRUISES?

I MUST HAVE SUPER HEALING OR SOMETHIN'!

WITH THAT, BATPIG ATTEMPTED TO MIND-LIFT REPTO-MAN INTO THE AIR.

BUT THE SLITHERY FIEND WAS TOO HEAVY!

SO MY "FROSTY the SNOWMAN THEORY" DIDN'T WORK.

I WAS SURE the HAT WAS THE SOURCE OF HIS POWER.

BATPIG NEEDED A SMART PLAN.

INSTEAD, HE GRABBED REPTO'S TAIL.

GOTCHA!

OUR HERO WAS KNOCKED OUT COLD!

UNFORTUNATELY, REPTO-MAN SMASH-LANDED THROUGH THE ROOF OF A GIANT-SPACE-ROCKETS-R-US.

CRASHH!

GIANT-SPACE-ROCKETS-R-US

SALE!

(I THINK WE ALL SEE WHERE THIS IS HEADED.)

BACK AT CARL'S, HIS MOM FOUND HIM DUCT-TAPED TO THE BED.

MPH!

CARLY-POO? WHY ARE YOU TAPED TO THE BED? AND WHY IS THERE A GIANT-LIZARD-SIZED HOLE IN THE WALL?

SHE RELEASED HIM, PULLING OFF A FEW SCALES IN THE PROCESS.

NO TIME TO EXPLAIN, MOM! GARY AND BROOK ARE IN TROUBLE!

BE CAREFUL, CARLY-POO!

CARL TOOK OFF AT A SPRINT.

CHAPTER NINE

IS IT CALLED "CATCHING UP TO THE PRESENT"? PLEASE?

"CALM DOWN. ALMOST THERE."

REPTO-MAN CAME OUT OF THE GIANT-SPACE-ROCKETS-R-US, HIS ARMS FULL.

WELL, THAT WORKED OUT GREAT FOR MY EVIL PLANS!

SPACE ROCKET KIT

THEN HE NOTICED THE STORE NEXT DOOR.

SERIOUSLY? WHAT ARE THE ODDS?

POISON PILL MART

SPACE ROCKET KIT

BACK DOWNTOWN, HE FOUND THE UNCONSCIOUS BATPIG (AS WELL AS HIS MAGICIAN'S HAT).

HE WENT TO THE TOP OF THE CLOSEST BUILDING TO ASSEMBLE HIS ROCKET.

GARY'S IN TROUBLE! I MEAN BATPIG!

I KNOW! I SAW ON THE NEWS!

HOW... HOW DO YOU KNOW ABOUT BATPIG?

I KNOW EVERYTHING, OKAY? WE'LL TALK ABOUT IT LATER!

101

CHAPTER TEN

"BACK TO EARTH"

BATPIG ONLY HAD MAYBE A MINUTE UNTIL IMPACT. HE WASN'T FEELING POSITIVE.

I MAY HAVE PEED A LITTLE.

HE HAD HIS EYES CLOSED TIGHT WHEN HE THOUGHT HE HEARD HIS NAME.

GARY!

WAS HE LOSING IT?

H...HELLO?

105

THEY LATCHED ONTO THE ROCKET AND CARL STARTED SAWING AWAY.

YOU GUYS CAME!

OF COURSE WE CAME, DUDE!

WE'RE GONNA DIE!

FINALLY, THE RESTRAINTS BROKE AWAY. JUST IN TIME.

BATPIG CARRIED BROOK AND CARL OUT OF HARM'S WAY AS THE ROCKET CRASHED.

BOOM

I'm OKAY. I'm OKAY. I'm OKAY.

109

AND WITH THAT, THEY HAD A PLAN.

BATPIG TOOK THE NASTY INGREDIENTS AND FLEW OFF TO FIND REPTO-MAN.

CHAPTER ELEVEN

"UNFINISHED BUSINESS"

BATPIG FOLLOWED THE TRAIL OF RUBBLE AND CHILI STRAIGHT TO REPTO-MAN.

WE MEET AGAIN, REPTO.

AAAAH, MISTER PIG. I'VE BEEN LOOKING FOR YOU.

MAYBE WE CAN HASH THIS OUT WHILE I'M **AWAKE** THIS TIME.

IT'S NOT MY FAULT YOU WERE SLEEPING ON THE JOB, SWINE.

BUT BATPIG HAD COME PREPARED.

REPTO-MAN WAS STUMPED. HE DIDN'T KNOW THIS ONE.

Because it GOT STUCK in a CRACK.

FOR a LONG MOMENT, THe HUGe LiZaRD SaiD NOTHiNG.

BUT THeN He SMiLeD aND BeGaN TO LaUGH.

HeH.

AND LAUGH... HA! A CRACK!

AND LaUGH. Ha! HA! HA!

THEN THE HORRIBLE FOE WAS CLUTCHING HIS SIDES...

OH, THAT'S GREAT. A BUTT CRACK!

AND ROLLING ON THE GROUND IN FITS OF LAUGHTER.

HAHAH

THAT'S WHEN BATPIG MADE HIS MOVE.

FIZZZZz

IT TOOK A SECOND, BUT THEN REPTO-MAN BEGAN TO SHRINK.

AW, FER CRYIN' OUT LOUD!

MY... WORDS... NOT... SPEAK...

POOP!

...

BATPIG SWEPT IN AND GRABBED THE COOL-RANCH-SCENTED BADDIE.

EW. STICKY.

HE FLEW BACK TO CARL AND BROOKLYN.

BAD LIZARD!

AND THEN THE THREE TOOK OFF FOR CARL'S TO PLAY VIDEO GAMES.

AND MAYBE SOME TASTY SANDWICHES?

SIGH.

YES, GARY, WE CAN HAVE SANDWICHES.

THE END

NO! WAIT! NOT THE END!

CARL AND BROOKLYN ARRIVED AT SCHOOL AS CARL FINISHED HIS WORM SMOOTHIE.

CARL'S MOM MADE THE BEST WORM SMOOTHIES ON THE PLANET.

GARY WAS WAITING (CONVENIENTLY) BY THE TRASH CAN BY THE FRONT DOOR.

MOMENTS LATER, JESSICA ANGELFISH, THE MOST POPULAR, COOL FISH IN SCHOOL (AND CARL'S CRUSH), WALKED UP TO HIM.

Hey, CARL.

SHE ACTUALLY SPOKE TO HIM!

UM...HELLO, JESSICA. HOW PERFECTLY NORMAL FOR YOU TO KNOW MY NAME!

HOW WAS YOUR WEEKEND?

CARL'S WEEKEND WAS SPENT SAVING THE CITY WITH BROOK AND GARY/BATPIG!

UM...

WHAT SHOULD HE DO? JESSICA NEVER SPOKE TO HIM, AND NOW HE HAD AN AMAZING STORY TO IMPRESS HER!

IT'S A SECRET! YOU PROMISED!!

TELL HER!! TELL HER!!

CARL STARTED SWEATING. (FISH SWEAT: EXTRA GROSS)

OH, NO! HERE IT COMES!

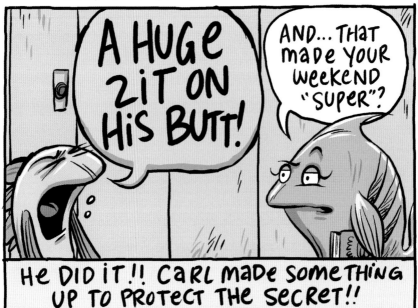

HE DID IT!! CARL MADE SOMETHING UP TO PROTECT THE SECRET!!

DURING THIRD PERIOD, BROOKLYN FOUND CARL HYDRATING IN THE BATHROOM.

CHAPTER ONE

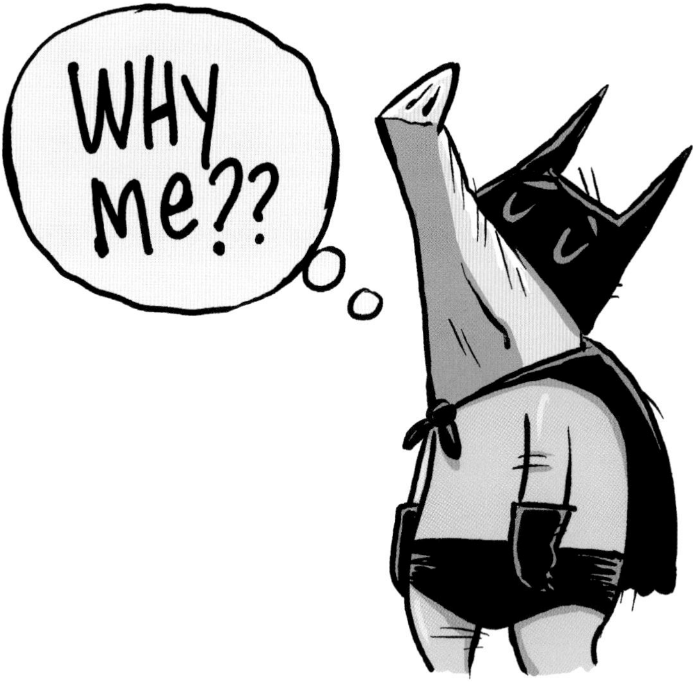

"A GOOD DAY RUINED"

OUR HERO, BATPIG, FOUND HIMSELF IN A HORRIBLE PREDICAMENT!

CURSES! WHY DOTH FATE HATE ME SO!!

He HaD STePPeD IN Some STiCKY GUM.

GRUMBLE... HeRO... NO ReSPeCT...

I MEAN, IT WaS SUPeR STiCKY.

LiKe, WaLK-HOMe-IN-ONe-BOOT STiCKY.

I WILL AVeNGe YOU, BOOT!

THE NEXT MORNING — WATCHING HIS STEP — GARY SET OUT FROM HIS BUILDING HEADED FOR SCHOOL.

WOW! IT'S A BEAUTIFUL DAY IN THE NEIGHBORHOOD!

UNFORTUNATELY, HE HAD TO PASS THE STORE NEXT DOOR..."THE MEAT LADY."

OH, MAN.

DO I CROSS THE STREET TO AVOID HER TODAY?

MEAT LAD

OPEN

NO! I'm GONNA GO FOR IT.

BUT JUST AS HE STARTED, THE MEAT LADY OPENED THE DOOR TO MAKE HER TERRIBLE MEAT JOKES.

HOW DID SHE ALWAYS KNOW WHEN GARY WAS ABOUT TO WALK BY?

He told Brook and Carl about it at lunch.

I don't know if she thinks it's funny or if she's just...

A jerk?

An evil jerk face?

Well, forget about her.

Yeah, we're gonna play "Super Mushers 3" at my house tonight.

Oh! You got it?? I heard it's mushier than 2!

But then Gary remembered...

Oh, no. Wait.

141

THE AWFULNESS OF WHAT HE HAD TO DO MADE HIS TAIL AND HOOVES GO ICE COLD.
I HAVE TO BABYSIT MY COUSIN TONIGHT.

143

MERVIN WAS, IN FACT, THE WORST.

I'M MERVIN!

SUPER-SPOILED MERVIN AND HIS FAMILY LIVED DOWN THE HALL FROM GARY AND HIS FAMILY.

MERVIN'S PLACE

GARY'S PLACE

MERVIN'S TANTRUMS WERE FAMOUS IN THE NEIGHBORHOOD, AND HIS WHINING COULD BE HEARD FROM SPACE.

BUT MOMMY, I WANT A BLUUUUE ONE! A BLUE ONE! BLUE! BLUE! NOOOOOOOO!!

He was the pickiest eater that ever lived.

He asked more questions than any kid alive.

And maybe worst of all...

He didn't like the Crimson Swine.

BUT, GARY HAD AGREED, SO AT 6:30 HE WAS READY, WAITING FOR THE KNOCK AT THE DOOR.

I'M NOT READY. I'M SO NOT READY.

KNOCK KNOCK

GARY'S PARENTS LEFT WITH HIS AUNT AND UNCLE.

STAY OUT OF TROUBLE! HA HA!

Ha.

AND THEN HE AND MERVIN WERE ALONE.

YOU'RE BORING.

WELL, YOU'RE AWFUL.

GARY TRIED TO COME UP WITH SOME ACTIVITIES.

147

CHAPTER TWO

"ASK AND YE SHALL RECEIVE"

IT WAS SETTLED. BROOK AND CARL SHOWED UP JUST A BIT LATER.

WHILE GARY CHANGED, HE COULD HEAR
MERVIN FLIPPING OUT IN THE OTHER ROOM.

AS THE BABYSAT,
I HAVE RIGHTS!

I DEMAND
PIZZA!

NO! TWO
PIZZAS!

HE WAS PUTTING ON HIS BOOTS WHEN
MERVIN BURST THROUGH THE BEDROOM DOOR.

WHOA. WHY ARE
YOU WEARING
A MASK AND
UNDERPANTS?

!

SLAM

CRIMS
SWINE

BUT CARL RAN IN AND SWEPT MERVIN OUT, MAKING UP A STORY ON THE SPOT.

Ha Ha! YOUR COUSIN GARY... HE, UM...

HE DOES SINGING AND DANCING TELEGRAMS... DRESSED AS A SUPERHERO.

SERiOUSLY?

(LOOK AT CARL KEEPING A SECRET! GO CARL!)

UM... YES? DO YOU BELIEVE ME?

I WANNA SEE IT.

SO GARY HAD TO DO A QUICK SONG AND DANCE BEFORE HE COULD LEAVE.

HA HA!

Have a RAZZ-ma TAZZ-ma Day!!

SHUFFLE

DANCE

BUT THEN HE WAS OFF TO FACE...
THE BUTCHER!!

WHICH IS WORSE? WATCHING MERVIN OR A SUPERVILLAIN?

IT WAS A TOSS-UP.

CHAPTER THREE

"SIZZLE, SIZZLE"

When Batpig reached the factory, he spotted the butcher, sitting atop the world-famous Yummy Yummy Biscuit sign on the roof.

OH, DEAR.

BIG CITY! I RULE THE BISCUITS!

YUMMY YUMMY

WHO COULD THIS MASKED VILLAIN BE??

THINK, BATPIG, THINK!

COME ON, NOGGIN!

AND WHY DID SHE HATE BISCUITS?

MEAT MY DEMANDS, OR THE FACTORY BURNS!

YUMM

↑SEE THAT? SHE SAID "MEAT" INSTEAD OF "MEET" 'CAUSE SHE'S A BUTCHER. LOL!

THE HORRIBLE VILLAIN WENT ON TO EXPLAIN WHAT SHE WANTED.

160

IT WENT ON LIKE THIS FOR A WHILE.

FINALLY, BATPIG GOT TIRED OF TALKING.

ALL RIGHT! I'M COMIN' TO GET YA.

BUT AS HE FLEW IN, HIS SNOUT PICKED UP AN ODOR.

OH!

SNIFF

OOF!

OH! GAH! WHAT IS THAT?

IT WAS BACON.

UH-OH.

MAY HURL!

HERE COMES LUNCH!

SERIOUSLY, THIS PART IS JUST GROSS.
CAN WE GO ON TO THE NEXT CHAPTER?

CHAPTER FOUR

"GIDDY-UP"

167

JUST THEN, GARY (HAVING FLOWN IN A HALL WINDOW) CAME THROUGH HIS FRONT DOOR LOOKING PRETTY ROUGH.
I THINK I FOUND MY KRYPTONITE.
WHERE'VE YOU BEEN? MUSTA BEEN A LONG SONG!
OH! GARY!! ARE YOU OKAY?
ARE YOU HURT? I WAS SO WORRIED!
JEEZ. IT WAS JUST A TELEGRAM.

So, Gary and Brook went off to discuss strategy while Mervin rolled Carl up in a place mat.

LOOK! LOOK AT THE WINDOW! YOU SEE HER TOO, RIGHT?

170

171

172

GARY'S HOOVES SHOOK AS HE OPENED THE TINY ENVELOPE.

CHAPTER FIVE

"UP, UP AND away"

177

180

CHAPTER SIX

"AAAAA!!"

DON'T TRY THIS AT HOME. DUH.

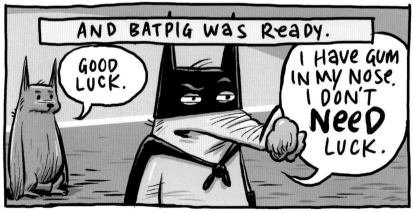

CHAPTER SEVEN

"FISH
BISCUIT"

ARRIVING BACK AT THE BISCUIT FACTORY, BATPIG SURVEYED THE SITUATION.

BUT, LET'S NOT FORGET ABOUT THOSE PIG POWERS. OR PIG-BAT POWERS OR WHATEVER...

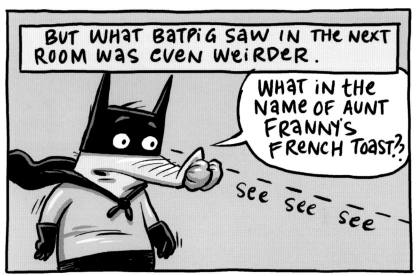

IT WAS A BUNCH OF GUYS DRESSED UP AS PORK CHOPS, PLAYING CARDS AND STUFF.

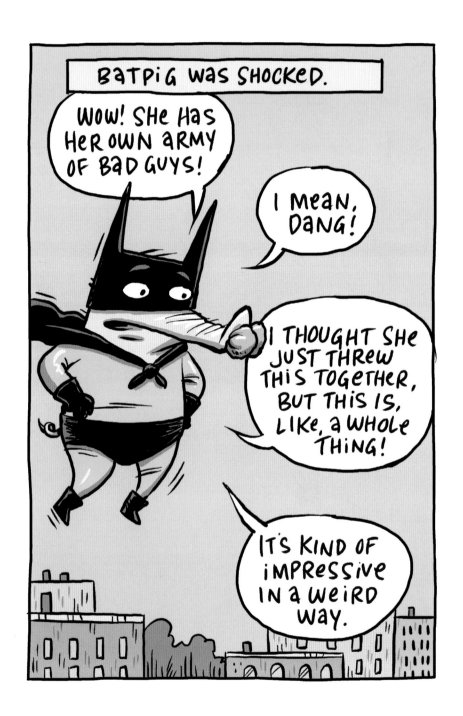

201

CHAPTER EIGHT

"SECRET WEAPON"

BROOK HAD (ONCE AGAIN) CONQUERED HER FEAR OF HEIGHTS AND FOLLOWED GARY.

WHILE NO ONE WAS LOOKING, SHE SNUCK IN THROUGH THE BIG HOLE BATPIG HAD LEFT.

SHE HAD A PLAN.

POPPING UP, SHE SIGNALED TO CARL TO BE QUIET.

TIMER ON!

NOOOO!

YESSS!

MMPH!

THEN WHISPERED TO MERVIN.

WHEN I PULL THIS DUCT TAPE, YOU'RE GONNA DO WHAT YOU DO, BUT LOUD, OKAY?

Hey, LADY! Ya BiG WeiRD LaDY aND YOUR JaNKY-LOoKiNG ROBOT! YOU THiNK YOU CaN SHUT Me UP, Ya BiG DUMPSTER-HeaD?!?

THE WHINING ECHOED IN THE FACTORY AND STUNNED THE BUTCHER AND HER ROBOT.

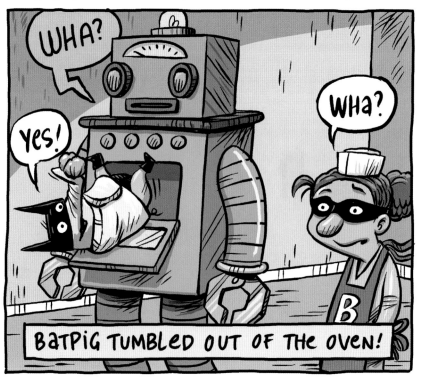

BATPIG TUMBLED OUT OF THE OVEN!

MERVIN KEPT IT UP, DRIVING THE ROBOT OUT OF ITS ROBOT MIND.

FINALLY, THE ROBOT COULDN'T TAKE IT AND BOUNDED OUT OF THE HOLE IN THE WALL.

I'M OUTTA HERE!

PIGS-IN-A-BLANKET ARE NASTY ANYWAY!!

THE BUTCHER TURNED TO RUN, BUT SLIPPED IN HER SPILLED HONEY MUSTARD.

DARN MY LOVE OF TASTY DIPS!

CARL AND BROOK THREW A GIANT WAD OF DOUGH ON TOP OF HER.

Hey!

WOO! HIGH FIVE!

BROOK RAN TO GARY AND FREED HIM FROM HIS "BLANKET."

SOME SUPERPIG I'M TURNING OUT TO BE.

THERE'S NO TIME, GARY! THAT ROBOT IS ON THE LOOSE!

I KNOW. PULL THESE GUM PLUGS. I'M GOING AFTER HIM.

CHAPTER NINE

"BLANKETS GALORE"

The answer was surprisingly clear.

SO BATPIG TOOK OFF FOLLOWING THE TRAIL OF THINGS-IN-BLANKETS.

FINALLY HE TURNED A CORNER AND FOUND THE ROBOT TRYING TO MAKE A NEWS STAND-IN-A-BLANKET.

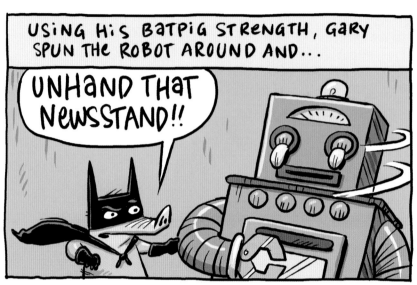

USING HIS BATPIG STRENGTH, GARY SPUN THE ROBOT AROUND AND...

UNHAND THAT NEWSSTAND!!

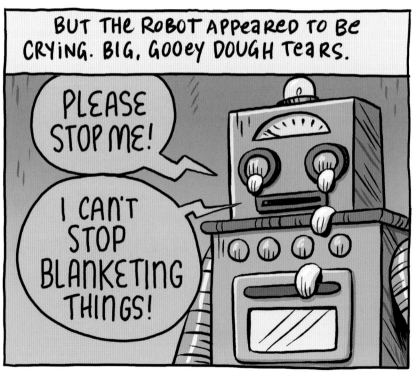

BUT THE ROBOT APPEARED TO BE CRYING. BIG, GOOEY DOUGH TEARS.

PLEASE STOP ME!

I CAN'T STOP BLANKETING THINGS!

FINALLY HE SOOTHED THE ROBOT A BIT WITH HIS NEW SUPER-SOOTHING POWERS. (WHO KNEW?) THE TWO SAT DOWN ON THE CURB.

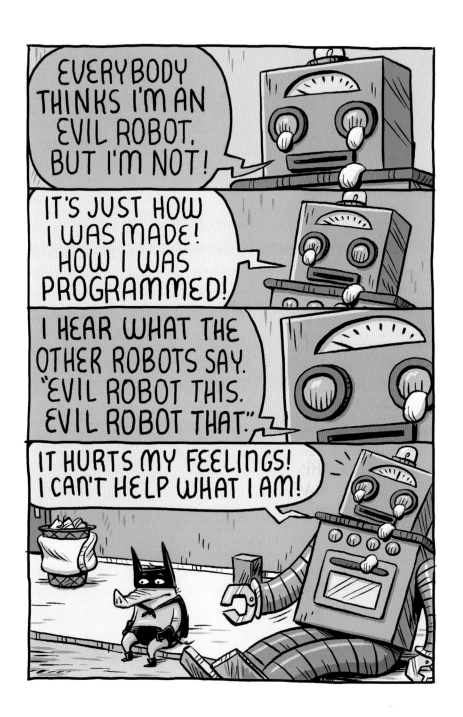

220

GARY THOUGHT ABOUT THAT FOR A BIT.

I UNDERSTAND, BLANKEY.

I REALLY DO.

THERE'S THIS MEAN WOMAN—"THE MEAT LADY"—IN MY NEIGHBORHOOD.

SHE'S ALWAYS MAKING MEAT AND PORK JOKES, JUST LIKE THIS BUTCHER VILLAIN.

BACON JOKES. HAM JOKES.

I CAN'T HELP THAT I'M MADE OF SUPER TASTY MEAT!!

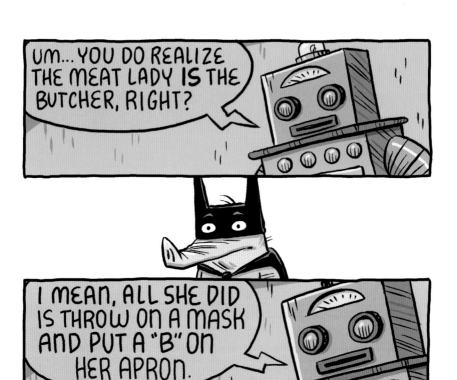

BUT... I JUST HAD A GREAT IDEA, BLANKEY.

THE TWO TOOK OFF, BATBIG FLOATING BLANKEY ALONG WITH HIS POWERS.

WHEE!

BATPIG LEFT BLANKEY WITH THE GOOD PEOPLE AT THE "VEGETARIAN PIGS-IN-A BLANKETS" FACTORY.

YOU CAN MAKE BLANKETS ALL DAY AND HARM NO ONE!

YAY!

GROOVY, MAN!

JUST THEN, GARY FLEW IN.

GUYS! ARE YOU ALL OKAY?

NO, BUT WE'RE NOT DEAD... SO THERE'S THAT.

HE TOLD THEM ABOUT HIS TALK WITH THE ROBOT, AND HIS SOLUTION.

VEGETARIAN PIGS-IN-A-BLANKET SOUND GROSS!

AND YOUR CAPE LOOKS WEIRD!

ALWAYS NICE TO HAVE YOUR INPUT, MERVIN.

KIND OF WEAK. YOU CAN DO BETTER.
HMM.
...LOCK YOU UP. THROW AWAY THE KIELBASA?...
...THROW YOU IN THE SALAMI-ER? INSTEAD OF SLAMMER??
MAYBE YOU JUST SKIP THE "WITTY FINAL WORDS TO THE CRIMINAL" THIS TIME.
YEAH.
IT'S FINE. REALLY. I GET IT.

CHAPTER TEN

"HOME"

YES, MERVIN. IF I'M GROUNDED FOR ETERNITY, HOW CAN I KEEP THE CITY SAFE FROM EVIL?

FINE.

CAN I BE YOUR SIDEKICK?

NO OFFENSE, BUT I'D RATHER HAVE A BAG OF ROTTEN CANTALOUPES AS MY SIDEKICK.

OKAY... SOLID BURN.

JUST THEN THEY HEARD KEYS IN THE DOOR, AND GARY'S PARENTS CAME IN.

THE END

THAT'S IT, READERS. UNTIL THE NEXT BOOK. LET'S JUST HOPE BATPIG DOESN'T GO AND GET COCKY OR ANYTHING.

TOO PiG TO FAiL

Gary Yorkshire is finally getting into the swing of this whole superhero thing: saving the world from terrible villains – and masterfully concealing his identity with a very small mask. But what happens when Batpig is called to battle time itself in a maths class that just won't end? Or when the city is attacked by something completely (and literally) out of this world?

It's not easy being a super-swine, but with the help of his best friends Brook the bat and Carl the fish, there's no hamburglar they can't catch.

LOOKING FOR MORE GREAT READS FROM WALKER BOOKS?

The first book in a fantastically funny series from the winner of the Lollies award.

Rex rules the prehistoric world, until a pesky ice age comes along and he finds himself frozen solid in a glacier. When he wakes up 65 million years later, things have changed – and to survive in the human world, he'll need a good disguise, the help of some other undercover creatures and ... a job!

ROB HARRELL (www.robharrell.com) created the Life of Zarf series, the graphic novel *Monster on the Hill*, and also writes and draws the long-running daily comic strip *Adam@Home*, which appears in more than 140 papers worldwide. He lives with his wife and pup in Indiana, USA.